Peter Patilla

At Home With MATHS

OXFORD
UNIVERSITY PRESS

Introduction

The *At Home With* workbooks introduce and reinforce key numeracy and literacy concepts for primary school children. They provide lots of opportunities to develop the key skills that are the basis of primary school curriculum work. The workbooks are available in three levels: 3–5 years, 5–7 years, and 7–9 years. The activities are fun and are designed to stimulate discussion, as well as practical skills. Some children will be able to complete the activities alone, after initial discussion; others may benefit from adult support throughout. All children will enjoy rewarding themselves with a sticker when they reach the end of an activity.

Using the book

- The words on the page are for you to read with your child.
- You'll see that each double page is devoted to a separate topic, and that each page is divided into three stages: Warm Up, Learn about, and Now try these. These give your child a natural progression through each topic; the Warm Up is always devoted to number work; the Learn about teaches a particular concept, and then Now try these gives a practical application.
- Important recording skills have been carefully introduced throughout the book. They include joining up, ticking, crossing out, simple colouring and drawing, as well as writing numbers.

Helping your child

- Do not expect your child to do too much at one sitting: a two-page spread is usually enough work.
- Although there is a mathematical development throughout the book, children do not always learn in an orderly way. They can pick single pages which appeal to them.
- If your child has a particular difficulty with an activity, don't make him or her anxious about it. Check whether it is a simple misunderstanding which can be explained, or something deeper.
- Most important, give plenty of praise and encouragement. Learning experiences such as these are meant to be fun as well as educational.

OXFORD
UNIVERSITY PRESS

Great Clarendon Street, Oxford OX2 6DP

Oxford University Press is a department of the University of Oxford.

Oxford is a registered trade mark of Oxford University Press
in the UK and in certain other countries

© Peter Patilla 2001
Edited and designed by Lodestone Publishing Limited, Uckfield, East Sussex
Illustrations by Rachel Fletcher

The moral rights of the author have been asserted

Database right Oxford University Press (maker)

First published 2001
Reissued 2009
This edition 2012

All rights reserved.

British Library Cataloguing in Publication Data

Data available

ISBN: 978 0 19 273331 3

10 9 8 7 6 5 4 3

Printed in China

Paper used in the production of this book is a natural, recyclable product made
from wood grown in sustainable forests. The manufacturing process conforms
to the environmental regulations of the country of origin

CONTENTS

Counting to 10

▼ Warm up

Trace over the numbers. Say the numbers.

0 1 2 3 4 5 6 7 8 9 10

◤ Learn about

Count each number in ones. Can you count them in twos?

▼ Now try these

How many pips are in each apple?

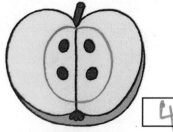 4

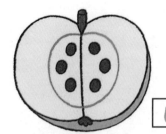 6

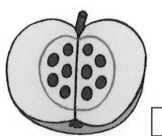 10

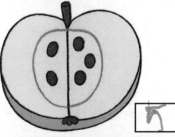 5

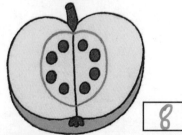 8

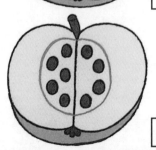 9

4

Counting to 10

▼ Warm up

What is the next number?

3 → 4   5 → 6   8 → 9

▼ Learn about

Make sure you can write the numbers properly.

0 1 2 3 4 5 6 7 8 9 10

▼ Now try these

Draw the same number of biscuits in the empty jar.
Write how many you have drawn.

  5

  7

 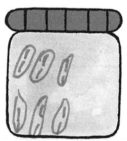 6

  4

Patterns

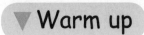

▼ Warm up

Say and trace these numbers.

0 2 3 5 7 8 9

Which numbers are missing up to 10?

Learn about

Patterns can be made from lines.

Look for patterns made from lines in your home.

▼ Now try these

Trace then continue these patterns.

Draw your own line pattern.

6

Patterns

▼ Warm up

Say and trace these numbers.

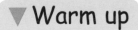

Which numbers are missing up to 10?

Learn about

Some patterns repeat.

Look for repeating patterns in your home.

▼ Now try these

Colour to continue each pattern.

Continue these patterns.

7

Shapes

What is the next number?

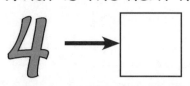 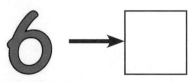 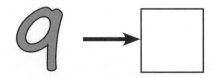

▼ Learn about

Learn the names of these shapes.

   triangle   circle   square   rectangle

▼ Now try these

There are 5 shapes in each set. Find and colour the odd one out. Write the name of the odd one out.

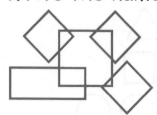
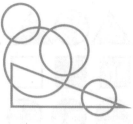

....

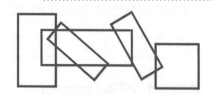

....

Shapes

▼ Warm up

Which number comes just before these?

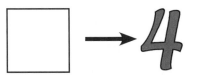 → **4** 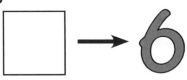 → **6** 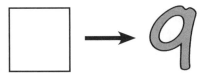 → **9**

Learn about

All these shapes are triangles. They each have 3 sides and 3 corners.

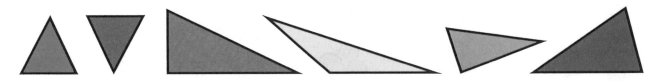

▼ Now try these

Join dots to make triangles. Colour them in.

. . . .
. . . .
. . . .
. . . .

Join shapes to their names.

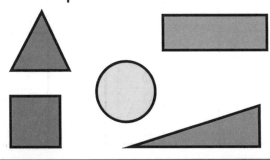

triangle

square

circle

rectangle

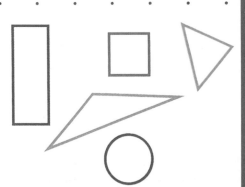

9

Adding

Which number is 1 more than these?

 3 → ☐   6 → ☐   8 → ☐   9 → ☐

Learn about

Adding is totalling how many are in two or more sets.

4 and 5 are 9 altogether

4 and 5 add up to 9

4 and 5 total 9

▼ Now try these

Cross out dominoes which do not have the same total as the first one.

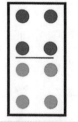   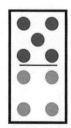   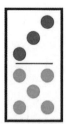   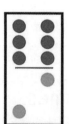   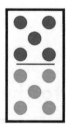   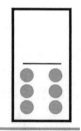

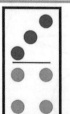   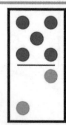   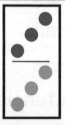         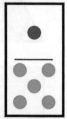

Adding

▼ Warm up

Which number is 2 more than these?

$0 \rightarrow$ ☐ $3 \rightarrow$ ☐ $7 \rightarrow$ ☐ $8 \rightarrow$ ☐

Learn about

We use the signs + and = when writing addition sums.

 and makes

$2 + 2 = 4$

▼ Now try these

Write an addition sum for each picture.

☐ + ☐ = ☐   ☐ + ☐ = ☐

☐ + ☐ = ☐   ☐ + ☐ = ☐

11

Measuring

▼ Warm up

Add 2 to each number.

1 → ☐   3 → ☐   4 → ☐   6 → ☐

▼ Learn about

We use these words when talking about measuring.

shorter   longer   shortest   longest

▼ Now try these

Tick (✓) the longest in each set.   Tick (✓) the shortest in each set.

Look at the 4 items in each set. Join them up in order of size.

12

Measuring

Add 2 to each number.

0 → ☐ **2** → ☐ **5** → ☐ **7** → ☐

▼ Learn about

We use these words when talking about measuring.

shorter   taller   same size   shortest   tallest

▼ Now try these

Tick (✓) flowers which are taller than the first.

Tick (✓) flowers which are the same height as the first.

13

Subtracting

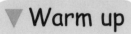 **Warm up**

Which number comes just before these?

Learn about

Subtracting is taking away one set from another and counting how many are left.

3 take away 1 leaves 2

3 subtract 1 is 2

Crossing out can help you find out how many are left.

Now try these

Pop 2 balloons from each set. Write the missing numbers.

take away 2 leaves

take away 2 leaves

subtract 2 is

subtract 2 is

Subtracting

▼ Warm up

3 bees fly away from each swarm. Write how many will be left.

Learn about

We use the signs − and = when writing subtraction sums.

5 take away 2 leaves 3

5 − 2 = 3

▼ Now try these

Write how many oranges will be left on the tree.

Pick 3 oranges   Pick 2 oranges   Pick 5 oranges

☐ − 3 = ☐   ☐ − 2 = ☐   ☐ − 5 = ☐

15

Counting

Write each of these words in numbers.

six .... three .... five .... seven ....

Learn about

We use these numbers when counting. Say the numbers.

1   2   3   4   5   6   7   8   9   10
11   12   13   14   15   16   17   18   19   20

▼ Now try these

Join numbers to words.   Join words to numbers.

12   4
8   eight   fifteen
           five   four   20
5   eighteen   eleven   11
18   twelve   twenty   15

Write the missing numbers on the birthday badges.

I am four today

I am nine today

I am thirteen today

Counting

▼ **Warm up**

Write each of these words in numbers.

zero .... two .... four .... ten ....

Learn about

You do not always start counting at 0 or 1.
You can start at any number.

3 4 5 6 7 ——→   9 10 11 12 13 ——→

Sometimes you have to count backwards.

10 9 8 7 6 ——→   20 19 18 17 16 ——→

▼ **Now try these**

Write in the missing numbers.

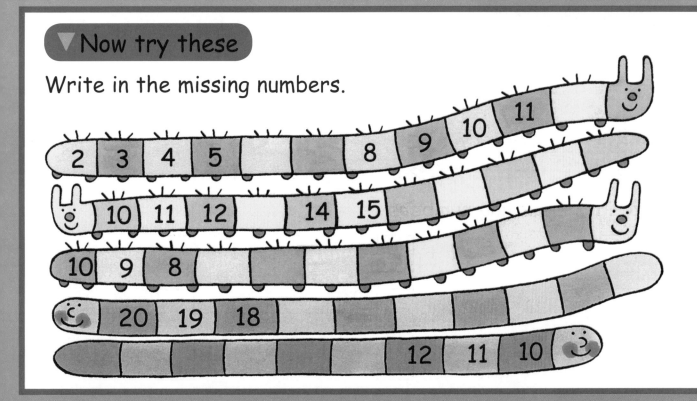

17

Number lines

▼ Warm up

Add 2 to each number.

0 → ☐ 3 → ☐ 4 → ☐ 6 → ☐

Learn about

Jumping forwards is the same as adding.

0 1 2 3 4 5 6 7 8 9 10

4 + 3 = 7

▼ Now try these

Use the number line above to help you.

3 + 3 = ...   3 + 4 = ...   8 + 2 = ...
4 + 5 = ...   5 + 2 = ...   4 + 4 = ...
5 + 5 = ...   6 + 4 = ...   6 + 3 = ...
2 + 3 = ...   7 + 2 = ...   9 + 1 = ...

Write in the missing numbers.

1 + ☐   1 + ☐   1 + ☐

2 + ☐ reaches 5   2 + ☐ reaches 7   2 + ☐ reaches 9

3 + ☐   3 + ☐   3 + ☐

Number lines

Subtract 2 from each number.

2 → ☐   **3** → ☐   **5** → ☐   **6** → ☐

Learn about

Jumping back is the same as subtracting.

0   1   2   3   4   5   6   7   8   9   10

$7 - 3 = 4$

▼ Now try these

Use the number line above to help you.

$5 - 3 =$	$7 - 4 =$	$6 - 3 =$ ....
$4 - 2 =$	$6 - 5 =$	$9 - 5 =$ ....
$7 - 2 =$	$8 - 3 =$	$9 - 4 =$ ....
$10 - 2 =$	$5 - 5 =$	$10 - 5 =$ ....

Write in the missing numbers.

$10 -$ ☐

$9 -$ ☐   reaches **5**

$8 -$ ☐

$10 -$ ☐

$9 -$ ☐   reaches **6**

$8 -$ ☐

$10 -$ ☐

$9 -$ ☐   reaches **2**

$8 -$ ☐

Money

▼ Warm up

Write the answers.

$3 + 3 =$ ☐ $4 + 4 =$ ☐ $5 + 5 =$ ☐

Learn about

You need to recognize coins.

1p   2p   5p   10p   20p   50p

▼ Now try these

Which coin above matches these?

  ➡ ☐ p   ➡ ☐ p    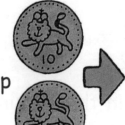 ➡ ☐ p

 ➡ ☐ p      ➡ ☐ p

20

Money

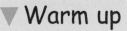

▼ Warm up

Write the answers.

2 + 3 = ☐   4 + 2 = ☐   2 + 5 = ☐

▼ Learn about

You sometimes need to add coins.

+ 3p   + 6p   + 7p

▼ Now try these

Write how much is in each purse.

   ☐ p

   ☐ p

Write these totals.

   ☐ p

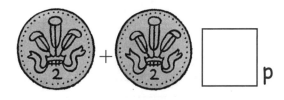   ☐ p

Shapes

Write the answers.

2 − 1 = ☐   4 − 2 = ☐   3 − 2 = ☐

Learn about

The same shape can come in different sizes and colours.

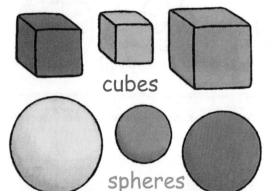

cubes

cylinders

spheres

cuboids

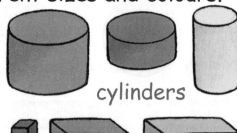

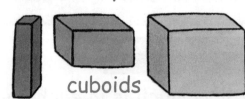

▼ Now try these

Draw a ring around the odd one out in each set.

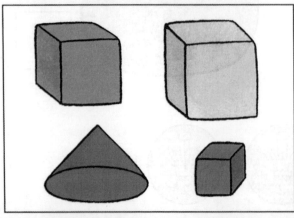

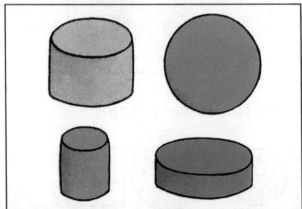

22

Shapes

▼ **Warm up**

Write the answers.

$5 - 1 =$ ☐ $5 - 2 =$ ☐ $5 - 3 =$ ☐

Learn about

Moving or turning a shape does not make it different.

cones

pyramids

▼ **Now try these**

Join shapes which match. The colour will be different.

Write names for 4 of the shapes.

....

23

Time

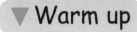

▼ Warm up

Write the answers.

6 + 0 = ☐   5 + 0 = ☐   9 + 0 = ☐

Learn about

The minute hand points to 12 at o'clock times.

The hour hand tells you which o'clock.

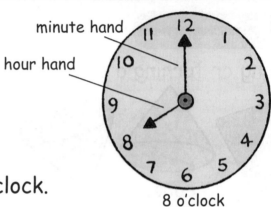

minute hand

hour hand

8 o'clock

▼ Now try these

Write the times under each clock.

☐ o'clock

☐ o'clock

☐ o'clock

☐ o'clock

☐ o'clock

☐ o'clock

Time

▼ Warm up

Write the answers.

$6 - 0 = \boxed{}$ $5 - 0 = \boxed{}$ $9 - 0 = \boxed{}$

Learn about

The minute hand points to 6 at half past times.

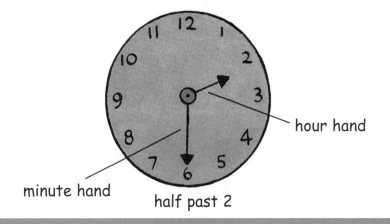

hour hand

minute hand

half past 2

▼ Now try these

Write the times under each clock.

half past $\boxed{}$

half past $\boxed{}$

half past $\boxed{}$

half past $\boxed{}$

half past $\boxed{}$

half past $\boxed{}$

Measures

Learn about

You use these words when talking about weight.

lighter   heavier   heavier   lighter

▼ Now try these

Tick (✓) the heavier in each pair.   Tick (✓) the lighter in each pair.

Measures

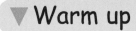 Warm up

10 – 6 = ...   10 – 7 = ...   10 – 8 = ...   10 – 9 = ...

Learn about

You use these words when talking about capacity.

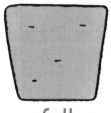         

full   empty   half full   nearly full

▼ Now try these

Colour each bottle to show how full it is.

full   nearly full   half full   nearly empty   empty

Join up the containers in order. Start with the one which holds least.

27

Numbers to 20

▼ Warm up

7 – 1 = ...   7 – 2 = ...   7 – 3 = ...   7 – 4 = ...

Learn about

Numbers can be broken up into tens and ones.

10 = 10 + 0   13 = 10 + 3   16 = 10 + 6   19 = 10 + 9
11 = 10 + 1   14 = 10 + 4   17 = 10 + 7   20 = 20 + 0
12 = 10 + 2   15 = 10 + 5   18 = 10 + 8   21 = 20 + 1

▼ Now try these

Write the missing numbers.

13 = 10 + ...   12 = ... + 2   14 = ... + 4
15 = 10 + ...   16 = ... + 6   17 = 10 + ...
18 = 10 + ...   19 = ... + 9   11 = ... + 1

Write in the missing numbers.

28

Numbers to 20

8 – 8 = ...   8 – 7 = ...   8 – 6 = ...   8 – 5 = ...

Learn about

You can add and subtract by jumping along a number line.

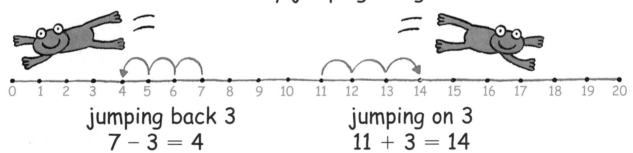

0 1 2 3 4 5 6 7 8 9 10 11 12 13 14 15 16 17 18 19 20

jumping back 3   jumping on 3
7 – 3 = 4   11 + 3 = 14

▼ Now try these

Write the missing numbers.

13 count on 3

15 count on 2

10 count on 5

16 count on 4

13 count back 2

16 count back 3

15 count back 5

20 count back 6

Information diagrams

▼ Warm up

What is 1 more than these?

11 → ☐   **13** → ☐   **16** → ☐   **19** → ☐

Learn about

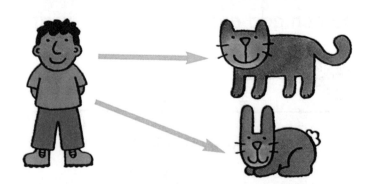

Some diagrams use arrows.

Tom has 2 pets.
He has a cat and a rabbit.

▼ Now try these

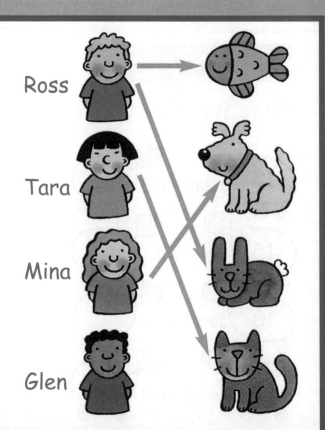

Ross

Tara

Mina

Glen

Who has 2 pets? ....

Which pet is Tara's? ....

Which pet is Mina's? ....

Who has a goldfish? ....

Glen's father gives him a dog.
Draw an arrow on the diagram
to show this.

30

Information diagrams

▼ Warm up

What is 1 less than these?

☐ →**11**   ☐ →**13**   ☐ →**16**   ☐ →**19**

Learn about

Some diagrams use pictures.

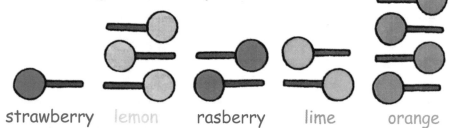

strawberry   lemon   rasberry   lime   orange

A teacher asked some children about their favourite lollies. This diagram shows what they said.

▼ Now try these

A teacher asked some children about their favourite sweets.

How many chose green? ....

How many chose purple? ....

How many chose yellow? ....

Which colour did only 1 person choose? ....

Which colour was most favourite? ....

red

yellow

green

blue

purple

31

Information

Numbers

0	zero				
1	one	•	11	eleven	
2	two		12	twelve	
3	three		13	thirteen	
4	four		14	fourteen	
5	five		15	fifteen	
6	six		16	sixteen	
7	seven		17	seventeen	
8	eight		18	eighteen	
9	nine		19	nineteen	
10	ten		20	twenty	

Shapes

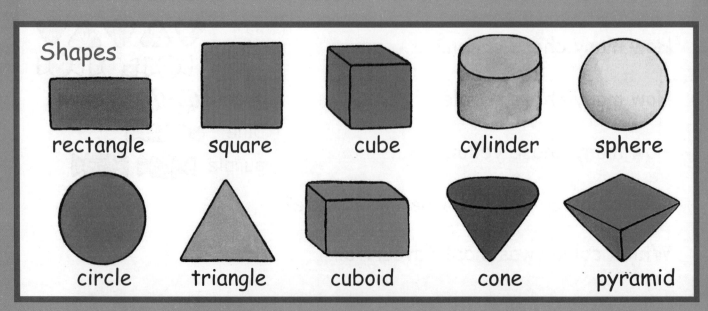

rectangle   square   cube   cylinder   sphere

circle   triangle   cuboid   cone   pyramid